# 1000 BIBLE QUESTIONS IN RHYMES, PUZZLES, QUIZZES & GAMES

Copyright 1932 by
Bowlby Press
Reprinted 1975 by
Baker Book House
with permission of the
copyright owner
Formerly published under the title,
*More Bible Quizzes*

ISBN: 0-8010-4136-8

Printed in the United States of America

# Contents

16. In Benjamin's place a slave he would be,
    But the viceroy of Egypt set them free.

17. At the ford of the Jordan his voice rang clear,
    "Repent, for the Kingdom now is here."

18. He worked seven years and won the wrong wife;
    He traveled to Egypt the last of his life.

19. In the temple at Shiloh he learned the things
    Which developed a boy to a maker of kings.

20. They locked him in town against his will,
    So he carried their gates to the top of a hill.

21. He set out for Damascus the Christians to slay,
    But his whole life was changed by a light on the way.

22. The father-in-law of a law-making man,
    Improved the courts by his share-the-work plan.

23. He set up an image where all men could see,
    And he said to the captives, "Now worship with me."

24. He knew how to preach, to condemn, to inspire;
    For his lips had been touched by the altar's fire.

25. A man of inadequate stature was he,
    Who talked with his Lord from the fork of a tree.

26. He wrote of love on the Gospel's page;
    An exile to Patmos, he died in old age.

27. They stoned him to death by a city wall,
    While he prayed that the Lord would forgive them all.

28. A priest by the altar, he lost his speech
    At the news of a son who was destined to preach.

29. Seeking the true religious light,
    He came to Jesus in the night.

30. All Israel mourned his tragic end;
    He was King David's noblest friend.

31. From this man's ancient prophecy
    The wise men learned where the Child should be.

32. Mary and Martha were wrapped in gloom,
    'Til Jesus raised him from the tomb.

33. Three years with the Master have ended in this —
A handful of coins for a traitor's kiss.

34. The son of the king, yet a rebel was he
When he swung by his hair from the limb of a tree.

35. In a stone-walled court where the fire blazed hot
He cried in his terror, "I knew Him not."

## 2. Who Are These Women?

1. The shepherds and sages adore and depart;
She quietly ponders these things in her heart.

2. She came with Naomi to Bethlehem,
And learned that a widow may love again.

3. She watched a princess find her brother,
Then for his nurse she brought his mother.

4. Two sisters kept at Bethany,
A home where Jesus loved to be.

5. They thought she would ask for jewels instead,
But the price of her dance was the prophet's head.

6. The water she drew for the stranger's beast
Entitled this girl to a marriage feast.

7. She came from afar as with banners unfurled,
To visit the wisest man in the world.

8. She helped him disobey the Lord,
And fled the fire of an angel's sword.

9. The body of her Lord was gone,
But he spoke her name in the Easter dawn.

10. The wife of a stern young prophet was she
Who redeemed her life from slavery.

11. She threatened the prophet Elijah's head;
But the scavengers licked her blood instead.

7

11. A marriage feast, a lack of wine;
    A guest who proved himself divine.

12. Famine was spreading everywhere,
    But this one land had corn to spare.

13. In the greatest metropolis of their day,
    Jews wept for a temple far away.

14. The deepest spot in the Holy Land,
    Where nothing grows but salts and sand.

15. The land where a Jewess rose to power,
    And saved her race in a tragic hour.

16. Three crosses stark against the sky,
    Where the Son of Man was left to die.

17. Solomon's temple and Herod's throne;
    A city Mohammedans claim for their own.

18. The shrine where Amos preached his dream
    Of "righteousness like a mighty stream."

19. A river that twists and turns as it goes;
    From Galilee the water flows.

20. Saints its glories shall behold;
    This heavenly city paved with gold.

# 5. True or False?

1. A church in Philadelphia is mentioned in the Bible.

2. Revelation is called the Apocrypha.

3. The smallest book in the Old Testament is Obadiah.

4. Nimrod was a "mighty hunter before the Lord."

5. The Jewish feast of Pentecost celebrated the deliverance of the Jew in the days of Esther.

6. Daniel was one of the three men in the fiery furnace.

7. There is a story in Genesis about a man who never died.

8. King David had only one wife.

9. Philip, the disciple, doubted that Jesus had risen until he saw the nailprints in His hands.

10. Samson pulled down the walls of Jericho.

11. Absalom led a rebellion against his father, King David.

12. The Bible says that money is the root of all evil.

13. David wrote all the Psalms.

14. Josiah was eight years old when he became king.

15. A lucky person is called a "Jonah."

16. Solomon's temple was built without noise.

17. St. Paul made tents for his living.

18. "Jots and nettles" means very small things.

19. The "unleavened bread" of the exodus was made without yeast.

20. "Thou shalt not lie" is one of the Commandments.

21. In Bible days leprosy was an incurable disease.

22. The Jewish Year of Jubilee came once in fifty years.

23. "Sackcloth and ashes" is a Biblical term for repentance.

24. Jezebel was a Phoenician princess.

25. Deborah cut off Samson's hair.

26. Another name for Daniel was Belteshazzar.

27. The people of Nazareth were called Nazarites.

28. The Jordan is a very crooked river.

29. Dagon was a god worshiped by the Philistines.

30. The Gospels tell how Jesus once made a trip to Rome.

31. At least forty parables of Jesus are recorded in the Scriptures.

32. The Sabbatical year of college professors is the seventh year, a period of rest.

33. Crucifixion was a common Jewish punishment.

31. Caesar's image on a coin.

32. A bow in the cloud.

33. A seal on a tomb.

34. A pillar of fire by night.

35. A pillar of salt.

36. A rock for a pillow.

37. Three white baskets on a man's head.

38. Thirty sheets and thirty changes of garments.

39. Six stone waterpots.

40. A silver cup in a sack of grain.

41. A ram in the bushes.

42. Five smooth pebbles.

43. A harp.

44. A fatted calf.

45. "Forty stripes save one."

46. A cloud the size of a man's hand.

47. One leper kneeling in the road.

48. An Ethiopian in a chariot.

49. Soldiers casting lots for a garment.

50. Moldy bread.

# 7. Bible Link Game

The object is to make a chain of names of Bible people or Bible places as long as possible. Each word is a link in the chain and each word must begin with the last letter of the previous word. For example, start with JERUSALEM. The next player says MARTHA. The third, ABRAHAM, etc. With a little practice you will learn to avoid words whose last letter makes it hard for the next fellow. For example, if the second player had said MARY instead of MARTHA it would have been hard to find a word beginning with a Y. In an emergency, common Biblical nouns like SACRIFICE, MYRRH, ALTAR, QUAIL, JUBILEE, etc., may be used.

## 8. What Did They Carry?

1. What did the Wise Men carry?

2. What did the women carry to the tomb on Easter morning?

3. What did David carry when he met Goliath?

4. What did Joseph carry the day his brothers decided to sell him?

5. What did Paul carry to the Gentiles?

6. What did Hannah carry every year to Shiloh?

7. What did Abraham carry when he led his young son Isaac up the mountain?

8. What did the seventy disciples carry when Jesus sent them out two by two?

9. What did the ten virgins carry?

10. What did the priests carry when they marched around Jericho?

11. What did Gideon's army carry?

12. What did Moses carry when he appeared before Pharaoh?

13. What did Pharaoh's baker carry on his head in a dream?

14. What did Nehemiah carry when he served the king?

15. What did Uriah carry for King David?

16. What did Peter carry to the Garden of Gethsemane?

17. What did twelve men carry when they crossed the Jordan into the Promised Land?

10. Purim, Passover, Tabernacles

11. Gold, frankincense, myrrh

12. Cana, Nazareth, Bethsaida

13. Hezekiah, Siloam, Bethesda

14. Altar of incense, table of shewbread, golden candlestick

15. Court of the Gentiles, Court of the Women, Holy of Holies

16. St. Paul's, St. Peter's, Notre Dame

17. Light of the World, Prince of Peace, Good Shepherd

18. David, Obed, Jesus

19. Hagar, Sarah, Keturah

20. Michal, Abigail, Bathsheba

# 11. Bible Number Game

The leader draws on the blackboard a large square marked off into smaller squares like a checkerboard. Have at least 25 squares. Ask the group to call out numbers and give their Biblical association. Write these numbers in the squares until all are filled. For example: 12 is the twelve disciples, 6 is the number of days in which the world was created, 40 is the number of years the Hebrews spent in the wilderness. The same number may appear twice on the board provided it has a different significance. Try to get as many different numbers as you can.

Another method is to draw a small circle on the board; around it draw two larger circles and divide these pie-fashion making two rows of about twelve spaces each around the center circle. Ask the audience to give you the largest number they can think of for the center. For example, 1611 the date of the King James Version of the Bible, or perhaps 5000, the number of people Jesus fed. Around this number, fill in the spaces with all the different numbers you can think of, telling where they occur in the Bible.

# 12. Pick the Right Answer

1. The city of Damascus was famous for _____ fish—steel—purple dyes.

2. "The beloved disciple" was _____ Simon Peter—Andrew—John.

3. Job was afflicted with _____ blindness—boils—leprosy.

4. A coat of many colors is associated with _____ Joseph—Moses—John the Baptist.

5. David played on a _____ trumpet—harp—flute.

6. Paul reached the island of Malta as the result of a _____ whirlwind—shipwreck—planned missionary journey.

7. Elijah disappeared in a _____ pillar of fire—chariot of fire—burning bush.

8. John the Baptist called his audience _____ "a generation of vipers"—"a valley of dry bones"—"scribes and Pharisees, hypocrites."

9. Which of these is NOT associated with the story of a lion? Samson—Daniel—Elijah.

10. "The lost cities of the plain" were _____ Dan and Beersheba—Sodom and Gomorrah—Nazareth and Capernaum.

11. Moses died on _____ Mt. Sinai—Mt. Ararat—Mt. Nebo.

12. We associate a slingshot with _____ David—Samson Gideon.

13. Manna was _____ a seamless garment—food in the wilderness—a month in the Jewish year.

14. The talents referred to in the parable were _____ the abilities of man—valuable coins—scrolls of the Law.

15. Zechariah is _____ a book in the Old Testament—the father of John the Baptist—a son of Jacob.

16. A covenant is _____ a Grecian robe—a solemn agreement—a small boat.

32. Which man in the Bible was hanged on a gallows he had built for his enemy?

33. Which man in the Bible was very patient and never lost his faith in God, no matter how many troubles he had to bear?

34. Which king wrote many of the psalms?

35. Why do the Jews celebrate Passover every year?

36. What is a synagogue?

37. Who followed a star across the desert until they found the baby Jesus?

38. When did a boy help Jesus perform a great miracle?

39. What does the word *Gospel* mean and what do you read in the Gospels?

40. Name the Gospels.

41. Where in the Bible would you find the story of Moses?

42. Which man ran away from home, slept on a rock in the wilderness and dreamed of angels on a ladder to heaven?

43. Give three names for the country where the Bible stories took place.

44. What happened on these three mountains: Ararat? Sinai? Nebo?

45. What does it mean to be crucified?

46. What was the prayer of Jesus for those who killed Him?

47. What do we mean by The Last Supper?

48. Which girl loved her mother-in-law so much that she refused to leave her?

49. Which boy in the Bible killed a giant with his slingshot?

50. Which prophet carried on the work of Elijah?

## 14. Can You Give the Third Word?

These words follow in familiar sequence. The number of spaces indicates the number of letters in the third word.

1.  Abraham, Isaac, and _ _ _ _ _?

2.  Shem, Ham, and _ _ _ _ _ _ _?

3.  Gold, frankincense, and _ _ _ _ _?

4.  "Scribes and Pharisees, _ _ _ _ _ _ _ _ _ _"?

5.  Shadrach, Meshach, and _ _ _ _ _ _ _ _?

6.  Father, Son, and _ _ _ _   _ _ _ _ _?

7.  Genesis, Exodus, _ _ _ _ _ _ _ _ _?

8.  "The leeks, the onions, and the _ _ _ _ _ _"?

9.  Galilee, Samaria, and _ _ _ _ _?

10. Saul, David, and _ _ _ _ _ _ _?

11. Peter, James, and _ _ _ _?

12. "The wind, the earthquake, and the _ _ _ _"?

## 15. A Quiz for Advanced Bible Students

1.  Is the word "Bible" in the Bible?

2.  What does the word *Bible* mean?

3.  In which two languages was the Bible first written?

4.  About how long did it probably take to write the Bible?

5.  Who wrote the Bible?

6.  Before the days of written language, how were the Bible stories preserved?

7.  Before the days of printing presses, how were Bibles made?

# 16. Can You Identify These Men and Women?

Which organization, achievement, or event do you associate with each of the following?

1. John Wesley
2. Martin Luther
3. Evangeline Booth
4. Jane Addams
5. John Huss
6. George Whitefield
7. Dr. Francis E. Clark
8. Brigham Young
9. Father Junipero
10. Booker T. Washington
11. Frances E. Willard
12. Dwight L. Moody
13. Robert Ingersoll
14. Mary Baker Eddy
15. Clara Barton
16. Henry Ward Beecher
17. Confucius
18. Mahatma Gandhi
19. John Calvin
20. Florence Nightingale
21. George Fox
22. Charles Darwin
23. William Lloyd Garrison
24. Gautama Buddha
25. Emanuel Swedenborg
26. John Bunyan
27. Henry M. Stanley
28. Charles Wesley
29. Francis Asbury
30. Charles Haddon Spurgeon
31. Julia Ward Howe
32. Lyman Abbott
33. Socrates
34. Constantine
35. Nero
36. Ann Judson
37. Cora Wilson Stewart
38. Dr. S. Parkes Cadman
39. Gypsy Smith
40. Spinoza

# 17. A Quiz on Religious Art

1. Have we any paintings of Jesus actually made in His lifetime?

2. What does the word *Madonna* mean?

3. Who painted *The Sistine Madonna?*

4. Who painted the famous *Immaculate Conception?*

5. Who painted *The Light of the World?*

6. Which Bible verse does it illustrate?

7. What is the most popular picture of the boy Jesus?

8. Who painted *The Last Supper?*

9. Raphael's *Madonna of the Chair* pictures the Mother and Child and one other character. Who is it?

10. In religious art, why is the circle symbolic of eternity?

11. Who painted the famous *Frieze of the Prophets* and where is it?

12. Which English artist is famous for his *Child Samuel?*

13. Where in America is the original of Hofmann's *The Rich Young Ruler?*

14. Which masterpiece of Rubens is connected with the crucifixion?

15. What modern artist painted about 400 pictures on the life of Christ, noted for their faithfulness to Oriental detail?

16. Who is famous for his statues of *David* and *Moses?*

17. Which Venetian artist was painting at the age of 99?

18. Who is considered the master of the fresco?

19. Who painted *Christ and the Fishermen?*

20. What and where is the world's largest religious picture?

# 20. A Missionary Quiz

1. Give the command of Jesus, the basis of all missionary work.

2. In the Early Church, who was "the apostle to the Gentiles"?

3. Name any three men who accompanied Paul on his missionary trips.

4. Which medical missionary "opened China at the point of a lancet"?

5. Who was the great missionary to Africa?

6. Which English cobbler became a famous misisonary to India?

7. In colonial days, who converted Indians near Boston?

8. Priests from which country established the missions of California?

9. Why was Africa called "the dark continent"?

10. Which missionary was active in stamping out the slave trade there?

11. Which Baptist missionary sailed from Salem, Massachusetts, to labor for God in the jungles of Burma?

12. Which general commanded Black troops in the Union Army in the Civil War and afterward founded Hampton Institute in Virginia to educate Black boys and girls?

13. Which modern English doctor consecrated his life to serve the natives of Labrador?

14. What are the "moonlight schools" and who started them?

15. Complete these names:

    (a) Adoniram _____

    (c) John G. _____

    (b) David _____

    (d) Sir Wilfred _____

16. Which missionary established the first hospital in Tibet?

17. With which country do you associate Dr. Robert Moffatt?

18. Which missionary gave his life at the age of 26 to stop a plague in Manchuria?

19. Which missionary dug the first well on the cannibal island of Aniwa in the New Hebrides?

20. What frail Scotch girl determined to be a missionary and spent forty years among the black head hunters of Calabar on the West Coast of Africa?

21. Which missionary do you associate with Afghanistan?

22. Who translated and printed the Bible for the Cree Indians?

23. Who was Alexander MacKay?

24. Who translated the Bible (or parts of it) into 34 native dialects of India?

25. Which Bishop of Minnesota was called "Straight Tongue" by the Sioux Indians because they said he was one white man who never lied to them?

26. Which Scotch missionary established the first mission school in India?

27. Which champion English cyclist founded a medical mission and industrial school at Aden, Arabia, and died at the age of 31?

28. Which Presbyterian missionary introduced domestic reindeer from Siberia into Alaska?

# 21. A Quiz on Religious Music

1. Which blind woman wrote hundreds of popular gospel hymns?

2. Which brother of which famous Christian leader is famous as a hymn writer?

3. Who wrote "A Mighty Fortress Is Our God"?

4. Who is associated, musically, with Billy Sunday?

5. Which Boston bishop wrote a Christmas carol, and what is the carol?

6. What are "waits"?

7. Which popular gospel song begins
   "On a hill far away . . ."?

8. Which hymn is based upon Jacob's dream in the wilderness?

9. How did the ancient Jewish church use Psalms?

10. How did the people learn them, without hymn books?

11. What is a cantor?

12. Which nation still sings Psalms twisted into rhymes and set to slow tunes?

13. Who wrote "Lead, Kindly Light"?

14. Which Christmas carol did Mme. Schumann-Heink sing nearly every year on the radio?

15. For what occasion did Kipling write his *Recessional?*

16. What musician, associated with light opera, wrote the music for *Onward, Christian Soldiers?*

17. Who wrote "The Battle Hymn of the Republic"?

18. Which hymn is credited to the Bishop of Cluny in the twelfth century?

19. What hymn reminds us of the story of Jesus' stilling the tempest on Galilee?

20. Which popular Christmas carol was written by Martin Luther?

21. Give the first line of the Doxology.

22. Which hymn tells about the persecutions of the early Christians?

23. What is the name given to a long musical composition on a religious theme, given with solos, choruses and orchestration but without scenery, costumes or action?

24. Is there any record in the Bible that Jesus and the disciples ever sang together?

25. Who is associated, musically, with Dwight L. Moody?

## 22. Questions for Well-Informed Christians

1.  What is a circuit rider?

2.  Does a "sky pilot" travel by airplane?

3.  Which popular preacher of John Wesley's day is buried in New-buryport, Massachusetts?

4.  Which famous and beautiful church is situated near Grant's Tomb in New York City?

5.  Which colonial minister, banished from Salem, Massachusetts, settled Providence, Rhode Island, and was formally pardoned by Salem on the 300th anniversary of Providence?

6.  Which colonial minister of Boston was involved in the persecution of the Salem witches?

7.  What does the word *catholic* mean in the Apostle's Creed?

8.  What religious significance has Hallow'een?

9.  At which season of the year is the New Orleans Mardi Gras held?

10. Do all Christians celebrate the birth of Christ on December 25?

11. What is a creed?

12. Did the Twelve Apostles formulate the Apostles' Creed, as we know it?

13. What part of a church is called the crypt?

14. Who was Sir Christopher Wren and for what is he famous?

15. Which tree is called the "Judas tree" and why?

16. Why did Stanley go to Africa?

17. Which American baseball player became famous as an evangelist?

18. Which state was settled by Mormons?

19. In European cemeteries the graves of Christians who died in the World War are marked by crosses. How are the graves of Jewish soldiers marked?

20. Which exiled sovereign was known as "The Lion of Judah"?

21. What is a tither?

22. What are the Goodwill Industries?

23. The Lord's Prayer consists of 66 words. Has anyone been able to put it into a very small space?

24. Which is the largest and most beautiful cathedral in Germany?

25. What is "The Christ of the Andes"?

26. What is the Vulgate?

27. What is the "breeches Bible"?

28. What are the Synoptic Gospels?

29. What is a Jeremiad?

30. From which church in Boston were the lanterns hung for Paul Revere?

# 23. These Are "Stickers"

1. Who was Antiochus Epiphanes?

2. Who were the Maccabees?

3. Who was Tiglath-Pileser?

4. When in the Bible did a lump of figs cure a boil?

5. Once Paul wrote a letter of introduction for a woman named Phoebe who was traveling to Ephesus. Where in the Bible is it?

6. Which book in the Bible was written to a woman?

7. Who is Tertius?

8. Solomon built the first temple at Jerusalem; who built the second?

9. Which early Church leader admonished the people to "love your brothers, revere God, honor the emperor"?

10. The Greek Homer was a poet. What was the Hebrew homer?

11. Name the "seven churches which are in Asia" as listed in Revelation.

12. If the King James version of the Bible is so excellent, why has it been necessary to spend time and money on several other versions since?

13. What priceless ancient manuscript of the Bible was found in a rubbish heap less than 100 years ago?

14. Who was Theophilus?

15. What was Joseph's wife's name?

16. Name the Four Horsemen of the Apocalypse.

17. Which ancient Hebrew enemy boasted 900 chariots of iron but died at the hands of a woman?

18. Who sang in prison at midnight?

19. What is Armageddon?

20. Which two books of the Bible start "In the beginning"?

# 24. Do You Know Your Hymns?

Can you give the next line or two of these familiar hymns and carols?

1. What a friend we have in Jesus

2. Onward, Christian soldiers, marching as to war

3. Just as I am, without one plea

4. From Greenland's icy mountains

5. Lead on, O King Eternal

6. I love to tell the story of unseen things above

7. O come, all ye faithful

8. We three kings of Orient are

9. There's a song in the air, there's a star in the sky

10. Savior, like a shepherd lead us

11. On a hill far away

12. Nearer, my God, to thee; nearer to thee

13. Jesus, Savior, pilot me

14. Brightly gleams our banner, pointing to the sky

15. It came upon the midnight clear

16. Yield not to temptation

17. Will there be any stars, any stars in my crown

18. When all my troubles and trials are o'er

19. Sweet hour of prayer, sweet hour of prayer

20. I need thee every hour, most gracious Lord

21. Watchman, tell us of the night

22. Rescue the perishing

23. Pass me not, Oh, gentle Savior, hear my humble cry

24. Master, no offering costly and sweet

25. Where cross the crowded ways of life

26. Holy, holy, holy! Lord God Almighty

27. O God, our help in ages past

28. There's a wideness in God's mercy

29. Let the whole creation cry

30. We plough the fields and scatter the good seed on the land

31. This is my Father's world, and to my listening ears

32. We would see Jesus, lo! His star is shining

33. Dear Lord and Father of mankind

34. I heard the voice of Jesus say

35. Now the day is over; night is drawing nigh

36. Day is dying in the west

37. Savior, again to thy dear name we raise

38. Break thou the bread of life, dear Lord, to me

39. Jesus calls us o'er the tumult
    Of our life's wild, restless sea

40. Faith of our fathers, holy faith

41. The son of God goes forth to war,
    A kingly crown to gain

42. Stand up, stand up, for Jesus

43. Oh, Master, let me walk with thee

44. Fling out the banner

45. Oh, Zion, haste, thy mission high fulfilling

46. O beautiful for spacious skies,
    For amber waves of grain

47. Mine eyes have seen the glory of the coming of the Lord

48. Hark, hark, my soul! angelic songs are swelling

49. The Church's one foundation

50. Blest be the tie that binds

51. Jesus shall reign where'er the sun

52. I love thy kingdom, Lord,
    The house of thine abode

53. Guide me, Oh, thou great Jehovah

54. Lead, kindly light, amid the encircling gloom

55. O Jesus, I have promised

56. Hark! the herald angels sing

57. Rock of Ages, cleft for me

58. When I survey the wondrous cross

59. In the cross of Christ I glory

60. Glory be to the Father,
    And to the Son, and to the Holy Ghost

# 25. Twenty Bible Questions

This is played like the familiar "Twenty Questions."

While one player is out of the room, the others agree on a character or place in the Bible. Then that player tries to guess it by asking not more than twenty questions of the players. Each question must be answered by Yes or No. Ask such questions as: "Is it a man?" "Is he a king?" "Is he a prophet?" "Is he in the Old Testament?" "Did he ever see Jesus?"

If the player discovers the right answer in less than twenty questions, he wins that number of points left (2 points for 18 questions). Then he chooses the next person to be "It." If he cannot get the right answer, he forfeits 20 points.

# 26. A Simple Bible Alphabet for Juniors

Spaces indicate the letters in each word.

| | | |
|---|---|---|
| A _ _ _ | | First man |
| B _ _ _ | | Heathen god |
| C _ _ _ | | First murderer |
| D _ _ _ _ | | Killed a giant |
| E _ _ _ _ | | Pharaoh's country |
| F _ _ _ _ | | What we must have in God |
| G _ _ _ _ _ | | They grew large in the Promised Land |
| H _ _ _ _ _ | | Samuel's mother |
| I _ _ _ _ | | His father nearly killed him on the mountain |
| J _ _ _ _ _ | | Led the people after Moses died |
| K _ _ _ | | Herod |
| L _ _ _ | | One of the Gospels |
| M _ _ _ _ _ | | Moses' sister |

| | |
|---|---|
| N _ _ _ | He built a big boat |
| O _ _ _ _ | Ruth's sister-in-law |
| P _ _ _ _ | Jesus called him "a rock" |
| Q _ _ _ _ | They ate them in the wilderness |
| R _ _ _ _ _ | Joseph's mother |
| S _ _ _ _ _ | The strong man |
| T _ _ | Commandments |
| U _ _ _ _ _ _ | The cry of the lepers |
| V _ _ _ _ _ | Queen of Persia before Esther |
| W _ _ _ _ _ | What Jesus did to the disciples' feet |
| Y _ _ _ _ | Joseph foretold seven—of famine |
| Z _ _ _ | A mountain in Jerusalem |

## 27. Which Word Is Out of Place?

One word in each group below is out of place and has no connection with the others in that series.

1. Which word is not mentioned in the Christmas story?
   Shepherds—ark—star—angels—manger

2. Which word is not in the Easter story?
   Gallows—tomb—garden—women—spices

3. Which word is not in the story of Noah?
   Ark—animals—snow—dove—rainbow

4. Which word is not in the story of the Wise Men?
   Herod—star—camels—shepherds—frankincense

5. Which is not one of the plagues of Egypt?
   Lice—frogs—boils—hail—leprosy

6.  Which is not one of the gospels?
    Matthew—Ezekiel—Luke—John—Mark

7.  Which is not a disciple?
    Simon Peter—Andrew—Micah—James—Thomas

8.  Which is not an Old Testament prophet?
    Isaiah—Lazarus—Jeremiah—Hosea—Amos

9.  Which is not one of the early Christian churches?
    Sardis—Pergamos—Joppa—Philadelphia—Smyrna

10. Which is not one of the twelve tribes?
    Lot—Dan—Gad—Judah—Benjamin

11. Which is not a woman?
    Esther—Michal—Rebecca—Ahab—Hannah—Jocobed

12. Which is not a book in the Old Testament?
    Genesis—Leviticus—Acts—Chronicles—Lamentations

13. Which is not one of Paul's letters?
    Joel—Timothy—Philemon—Ephesians—Titus

14. Which is not a city Paul visited?
    Antioch—Nineveh—Athens—Berea—Lystra

15. Which musical instrument is not mentioned in the Bible?
    Harp—violin—trumpet—saxaphone—cymbals—lyre

16. Which is not a city of Galilee?
    Nazareth—Capernaum—Ur—Cana—Bethsaida

17. Which animal is not mentioned in the Bible?
    Camel—lion—goat—fox—leopard—tiger—bear

18. Which is not a mountain of the Bible?
    Hermon—Sinai—Nebo—Everest—Carmel—Ararat

19. Which weapon is not mentioned in the Bible?
    Sword—spear—slingshot—pistol—lance

20. Which word is not connected with worship?
    Altar—shrine—Ark of the Covenant—chariot—priest

21. Which is not a Biblical measure?
    Cubit—homer—ephod—bath—ephah

22. Which is not a woman?
    Jesse—Sapphira—Jemima—Keren-happuch—Lydia

23. Which is not a man?
    Zebedee—Zacharias—Jezebel—Jeroboam—Jude

24. Which word is not found in the 23rd Psalm?
    Shepherd—staff—tabernacle—rod—table—cup

25. Which word is not found in the Lord's Prayer?
    Heaven—temple—bread—evil—glory

# 28. My Story of Joseph

Can you fill these blanks with the correct words?

Jacob had _____ sons. He loved _____ best and gave him a _____ of many _____. This made his brothers _____. When they got a chance, they hid him in a _____ and then they _____ him to some traders who took him away to _____. The brothers stained Joseph's _____ with _____ and told their father _____.

In Egypt, Joseph was a _____ in the house of the _____ of the king's guard. A wicked _____ lied about him and had him sent to _____. But he was such a _____ prisoner that he used to help the _____ with the other _____. Among them were Pharaoh's _____ and his _____. One night they had strange _____. Joseph told them what would happen and it _____.

Then Pharaoh himself dreamed about seven _____ and

'seven ears of _____. No one could explain it until the butler remembered _____. So they brought him from the _____. He told Pharaoh there would be seven _____ of          and          years of          so he must build big _____ and store up the _____ so his people would not _____. Pharaoh put Joseph in charge of this work, gave him fine _____ to wear, a ring for his _____ and a _____ to ride in.

In the famine, Joseph's _____ came to _____ to buy _____. Joseph knew _____ but they did not _____. He told them to bring young _____ next time. Jacob did not want to let _____ go but they were all hungry and his brother promised to _____.

Joseph gave a dinner for his _____ and the best _____ for Benjamin. Then he told his _____ to hide his silver _____ in _____'s sack. When they started home they were arrested. They were so sure they were inno-cent that they promised the one who had stolen the _____ would stay in Egypt and be a _____ always. To their horror, the _____ was found in Benjamin's _____. But ALL of them went back and Judah begged to be a slave instead of _____. Then Joseph knew they were no longer cruel and he cried, "I am _____ your brother. Come and live with me in _____." And they were happy together again.

42

## 29. Ten Bible Triangles

To make a triangle, start with one long word written vertically, one letter under another. Then fill in the smaller words. The first line is always one letter; the second, two letters; the third, three letters; and so on. The result is a right angle triangle. See how many you can make up.

### First Triangle

1. Begins with J. The good man who gave Jesus his tomb. 6 letters.

2. A king of Bashan (I Kings 4:19).

3. The _ _ _ of Galilee.

4. "Deliver us from _ _ _ _"

5. Simon's other name.

6. "Our Father, who art in _ _ _ _ _ _"

### Second Triangle

1. Begins with C. The kind of work Jesus did for his living in Galilee.

2. "Forgive us our trespasses _ _ we forgive"

3. The color of Esau's hair.

4. A tree of Palestine.

5. What the tomb was on Easter morning.

6. His leprosy was cured by bathing in the Jordan.

7. One of Paul's helpers.

8. Paul's letters are called this.

9. A quiet, worshipful manner.

### Third Triangle

1. Begins with M. Food the Hebrews ate in the wilderness.

2. "_ _ it was in the beginning"

3. "Thou shalt _ _ _ steal"

43

4. Mountain where Moses died.

5. Moses' brother.

## Fourth Triangle

1 Begins with V. The kind of drink they gave Jesus on the cross.

2. "Where _ _ he that is born King of the Jews?"

3. Used for catching fish.

4. "I will lift up my _ _ _ _ to the hills"

5. A burial place.

6. To pour oil on the head.

7. Biblical word for clothing.

## Fifth Triangle

1. Begins with T. Moses' church in the wilderness.

2. The voice at the burning bush, "I _ _ that I _ _."

3. "Take up thy _ _ _ and walk."

4. He took the mess of pottage.

5. "The Lord is not here, he is _ _ _ _ _."

6. Can a camel go through the eye of a _ _ _ _ _ _?

7. Another word for disciple.

8. Rich people rode in them.

9. It means "weeping or feeling sad."

10. Gave more courage to.

## Sixth Triangle

1. Begins with A. Esther's husband, the king of Persia.

2. Personal pronoun.

3. "Go to the _ _ _, thou sluggard."

4. What the angels did when Jesus was born.

5. What relation was Mordecai to Esther?

6. Queen who saved the Hebrews.

7. Be glad.

8. Not according to law.

9. The kind of clothes in which they wrapped the baby Jesus.

## Seventh Triangle

1. Begins with B. The "blessed are's" of Jesus.

2. A man mentioned in Gen. 38:3.

3. "_ _ _ and ye shall receive."

4. To work hard.

5. Gods made of wood.

6. What Jonah bought, to Tarshish.

7. On an altar at Athens, "To the _ _ _ _ _ _ _ god."

8. A follower of Jesus.

9. The people of Egypt.

10. Jewish churches.

## Eighth Triangle

1. Begins with T. A word from the Lord's Prayer meaning sins.

2. The first syllable of "repent."

3. A female sheep, in Nathan's parable.

4. Covering for the foot.

5. Jesus was called "the Prince of _ _ _ _ _."

6. City where Paul preached, in Greece.

7. The Bible's wisest man.

8. Military men.

9. A dark skinned man from northern Africa.

10. To make stronger.

1. Begins with Z. A short man who climbed a tree to see Jesus.

2. A city of Canaan (Joshua 7:14).

3. What they did to Samson's hair.

4. What Joseph wore, of many colors.

5. A wicked New Testament king.

6. He carried on Elijah's work.

7. The cry of the lepers.

8. Samson had great _ _ _ _ _ _ _ _.

## Tenth Triangle

1. Begins with M. A crowd of people.

2. "Lead _ _ not into temptation."

3. A boy.

4. "O Little _ _ _ _ of Bethlehem."

5. Jacob's father.

6. What the king sits on.

7. Righteous and straight.

8. Jesus healed all kinds.

9. Their tusks are ivory.

# 30. Who? What? Where? Which?

Supply the answers to the questions below and fill in the spaces with the missing words. The numbers of dashes indicates the letters in each word.

1. Who saw _ _ _ _ _ _ on a _ _ _ _ _ _ reaching to _ _ _ _ _ _?

2. Who blew their _ _ _ _ _ _ _ _ how many times and the walls of what city fell down?

3. Which two people saw whom on the road from Jerusalem to Jericho and passed by on the _ _ _ _ _  _ _ _ _?

4. Who had compassion on him, did what to help him, took him where, and said what?

5. Who saw his friend and teacher,           , carried off to _ _ _ _ _ _ in a _ _ _ _ _ _ _ of _ _ _ _?

6. Who said to the people at the _ _ _ _ _ _ river, "One comes after me the _ _ _ _ _ _ of whose _ _ _ _ I am not worthy to unlace"?

7. Who killed a _ _ _ _ with his bare hands and afterward found _ _ _ _ _ of _ _ _ _ in the carcass?

8. Who led the people back from _ _ _ _ _ _ _ to rebuild the walls of _ _ _ _ _ _ _ _ _?

9. Who put whom in a den of _ _ _ _ _?

10. Which people in the wilderness received food from _ _ _ and called it _ _ _ _ _?

11. Which son of David led a _ _ _ _ _ _ _ _ _ against him and died hanging from a _ _ _ _ by his long _ _ _ _?

12. Who came from what country, worked in whose field as a _ _ _ _ _ _ _ and later married him?

13. Who lived how many days in the stomach of a great _ _ _ _?

14. Who impersonated whom to secure his blind father's _ _ _ _ _ _ _ _?

15. At the banquet of which king a mysterious _ _ _ _ appeared writing strange _ _ _ _ _ on the _ _ _ _?

16. At the ford of which river did who baptize whom?

17. Who challenged whom to a contest on Mount _ _ _ _ _ _ to decide the power of the true God?

18. Who led what people _ _ _ _ _ years on the way from Egypt to where?

19. Who died on what mountain and nobody knows where he is buried?

20. Which people crossed the _ _ _ sea in safety and whose army following them was drowned?

21. Who was hanged on a _ _ _ _ _ _ _ he had built for his enemy?

22. Who fed 5000 with how many _ _ _ _ _ _ and how many _ _ _ _ _ _?

23. Which king had a man named _ _ _ _ _ killed in battle so he could do what?

24. Which queen went to plead with what king for her people, the _ _ _ _, and what did he hold toward her as a token of his favor?

25. Which ruler of Egypt dreamed of seven _ _ _ _ _ _ _ and seven _ _ _ _ _ _ _ _ and who told him what the dream meant?

# Answers

## 1. WHO ARE THESE MEN?

1. Noah
2. David
3. Abraham
4. Daniel
5. Belshazzar
6. Jesus
7. Saul
8. Boaz
9. Methuselah
10. Joseph
11. Joshua
12. Naaman
13. Elijah
14. Jeremiah
15. Moses
16. Judah
17. John the Baptist
18. Jacob
19. Samuel
20. Samson
21. Paul (Saul)
22. Jethro (Moses' father-in-law)
23. Nebuchadnezzar
24. Isaiah
25. Zacchaeus
26. John
27. Stephen
28. Zacharias
29. Nicodemus
30. Jonathan
31. Micah
32. Lazarus
33. Judas
34. Absalom
35. Peter

## 2. WHO ARE THESE WOMEN?

1. Mary
2. Ruth
3. Miriam
4. Mary and Martha
5. Salome (daughter of Herodias)
6. Rebecca
7. Queen of Sheba
8. Eve
9. Mary Magdalene
10. Gomer (wife of Hosea)
11. Jezebel
12. Claudia (wife of Pilate)
13. Dorcas
14. Esther
15. Lydia
16. Deborah
17. Rachel
18. Lot's wife

## 3. LESS FAMILIAR BIBLE MEN

1. Ananias
2. Pilate
3. Barnabas
4. Esau (Jacob's brother)

5. Aaron
6. The priest and the Levite in the parable of the Good Samaritan
7. Joseph of Arimathea
8. Haman
9. Eli
10. Shadrach, Meshach, Abednego
11. Simeon
12. Barrabbas

## 4. PLACES IN BIBLE GEOGRAPHY

1. Jericho
2. Mt. Sinai
3. Capernaum
4. Rome
5. Nazareth
6. Bethlehem
7. Mt. Nebo
8. Mt. Ararat
9. Gethsemane
10. Samaria
11. Cana
12. Egypt
13. Babylon
14. Dead Sea
15. Persia
16. Calvary
17. Jerusalem
18. Bethel
19. Jordan River
20. The New Jerusalem

## 5. TRUE OR FALSE

1. True. Rev. 1:11. This Philadelphia is a city of Asia Minor.
2. False—Apocalypse
3. True
4. True
5. False—Purim
6. False
7. True—The man was Enoch and God took him out of the world by "translation" instead of death. See Hebrews 11:5.
8. False—He had about eight.
9. False—Thomas.
10. False—Temple of Gaza.
11. True
12. False—"The LOVE of money." (I Tim. 6:10)
13. False—He wrote many of them.
14. True—II Kings 22:1.
15. False—An unlucky person.
16. True—I Kings 6:7.
17. True
18. False—The expression is "jots and tittles." Nettles are thorny weeds.

19. True
20. False—There is no specific commandment against lying. Exodus 20:16 forbids bearing false witness against one's neighbor.
21. False—Lev. 14 proves that leprosy was frequently healed although it was contagious.
22. True—Lev. 25:8-16.
23. True
24. True
26. True
25. False—Delilah was the lady involved.
27. False—Nazarites were a religious order in the Old Testament. Citizens of Nazareth were called Nazarenes.
28. True—In the course of 125 miles, it measures nearly 30 miles.
29. True
30. False
31. True
32. True
33. False—It was a Roman punishment.
34. False—Mount Moriah.
35. False
36. False—Mount Nebo.
37. True
38. True
39. False—Sixth day.
40. True
41. False—Galilee.
42. True
43. True
44. True
45. True
46. False
47. True
48. True
49. False—12 tribes.
50. False—So be it.

## 6. OF WHAT DO THESE REMIND YOU?

1. Jesus.
2. Peter, and Jesus' prophecy that Peter would deny him before the rooster crowed.
3. Moses.

4. Gideon's army. (See Judg. 7.)
5. Elijah's prophecy to King Ahab, "Where the dogs lick the blood of Naboth, there shall they also lick thy blood." Also the dogs which "ate Queen Jezebel" after she threw herself from the parapet into the street by the wall of Jezreel.
6. Gideon (See Judg. 6).
7. Saul consulted the witch of Endor. (I Sam. 28.)
8. The food which John the Baptist ate in the wilderness near the Jordan.
9. Haman built it for his enemy, Mordecai, but was hanged on it himself.
10. The foolish virgins in Jesus' parable.
11. Noah sent them out of the ark to see what the weather and flood conditions were.
12. Elisha and the poor widow. (See II Kings 4.)
13. It was on an altar on Mars Hill, Athens. Paul took those words for the text of his address to the Athenians.
14. Jesus and some of His disciples, after the resurrection. (John 21.)
15. Peter dreamed about it in the house of Simon the tanner at Joppa. It contained all kinds of animals, "clean and unclean," and Peter took it as a sign that the gospel was for Gentiles as well as for Jews. (Acts 10.)
16. Judas' reward for betraying Jesus.
17. Samson.
18. They were on the top of the Ark of the Covenant.
19. The gifts of a famine-stricken land, which Jacob sent to the viceroy of Egypt.
20. Jacob, when he impersonated his brother Esau.
21. Elijah, at the contest on Mount Carmel.
22. They were taken from the river bed by the various tribes when they entered the Promised Land, and the stones were left on the bank as a memorial of the occasion.
23. The New Jerusalem, as described by John in Revelation.
24. Mentioned in Revelation 13. Possibly an allegory of Nero.
25. Jesus sent the disciples to bring it, that he might ride into Jerusalem. (The triumphal entry.)
26. Balaam. (Num. 22:22-30.)
27. Jonah. (Chapter 4:5-7.)
28. Furnishings which the kind woman put in Elisha's room in her home.
29. Pharaoh gave them to Joseph when he made him viceroy of Egypt.
30. The price which Hosea said he paid to redeem his wife, Gomer, from slavery.
31. Jesus. (Matt. 22:15-22.)
32. Noah (rainbow).

33. Jesus.
34. It led the Hebrews in the wilderness.
35. Lot's wife.
36. Jacob.
37. Pharaoh's baker dreamed of them while he was in prison with Joseph. (Gen. 40:16-19.)
38. Samson's wager that thirty young men could not guess his riddle. To pay his bet, he killed thirty other men and took off their clothes. (Judg. 14.)
39. The wedding at Cana, where Jesus changed water into wine to save his hostess embarrassment.
40. Joseph's cup hidden in Benjamin's sack.
41. Abraham sacrificed it instead of his own son, Isaac.
42. David took them from the brook to use in his slingshot when he killed Goliath.
43. David.
44. The Prodigal Son.
45. Paul. (II Cor. 11:24.)
46. Elijah. (I Kings 18:44.)
47. Jesus and the nine ungrateful lepers.
48. Phillip. (Acts 8:26-39.)
49. Jesus—at the cross.
50. The men of Gibeon. (Josh. 9:5-12.)


## 8.   WHAT DID THEY CARRY?

1. Gifts: gold, frankincense and myrrh
2. Oils and spices to anoint the body of Jesus
3. A slingshot and five smooth stones
4. Food for his brothers
5. The Gospel
6. A little garment for Samuel
7. A knife
8. "Neither purse, nor script, nor shoes" (Luke 10:4)
9. Lamps
10. Trumpets (Rams' horns)
11. Lamps (torches) in pitchers
12. A rod
13. Three white baskets, the top one containing food
14. A cup. (He was the king's cupbearer)
15. A message to his captain that he was to be killed in battle
16. A sword
17. Twelve stones from the river bed, from which they built a memorial on the shore

18. The Ark of the Covenant
19. The man who was sick of the palsy
20. Bread and cheese
21. Captives and spoils of war
22. The head of John the Baptist
23. The baby Jesus
24. The cross for Jesus
25. "The lambs in his bosom" (Isa. 40:11)
26. The money bag
27. The bones of Joseph

## 9. WHO? WHAT? WHERE? WHICH?

1. Hannah—Samuel—Lord—Shiloh—Eli
2. Cain—keeper
3. Jacob—coat—colors
4. Noah—ark—Mount Ararat
5. Noah—dove—ark—waters
6. Moses—bush
7. Goliath—Israelites—David—slingshot
8. Jacob—stone
9. Rebekah—Jacob—Isaac—kids
10. God—rainbow—sky
11. Isaiah—coal—altar
12. Saul—David—harp
13. Joshua—sun—moon—stand
14. covenant—angels—wings
15. The Shunammite woman's son—seven—Elisha

## 10. WHAT DO THESE HAVE IN COMMON?

1. Joseph interpreted their dreams
2. Sons of Jacob
3. Enemies of the Hebrews in the Promised Land
4. Eighth century prophets
5. Translators of the Bible into English
6. Hebrew measures of length
7. Biblical cities of refuge
8. They caused the death of Sisera
9. Kings of Judah
10. Jewish festivals
11. Gifts of the wise men

12. Cities of Galilee
13. Famous pools in Jerusalem
14. Furnishings of the tabernacle
15. Divisions of Herod's temple
16. Famous European churches
17. Names applied to Jesus
18. All born in Bethlehem
19. Wives of Abraham
20. Wives of David

## 12. PICK THE RIGHT ANSWER

1. steel
2. John
3. boils
4. Joseph
5. harp
6. shipwreck
7. chariot of fire
8. "a generation of vipers"
9. Elijah
10. Sodom and Gomorrah
11. Mount Nebo. (Supposedly, no one knows where he is buried)
12. David
13. food in the wilderness
14. a valuable coin. A silver talent was worth more than $1000. The idea of making the most of our abilities carries out the true meaning of the parable, but to Jesus' audience a talent was a coin. One man in the story buried it in the earth.
15. a book in the Old Testament
16. a solemn agreement
17. David
18. Nicodemus
19. Eli
20. Antioch
21. a perfume
22. a book in the Old Testament
23. stoned to death
24. Abigail
25. Ephraim

## 13.  A QUIZ FOR BOYS AND GIRLS

1. Methuselah
2. Samson
3. Solomon
4. David
5. Joseph
6. Samuel
7. Bethlehem of Judea, near Jerusalem
8. Nazareth, in Galilee
9. Exodus 20
10. Elijah (and the prophets of Baal)
11. Jacob
12. John the Baptist
13. 150
14. The Old Testament
15. The Old Testament was written before Jesus was born and the New Testament after Jesus was born
16. The Lord's Prayer
17. The Sermon on the Mount. Jesus. (As recorded in Matthew, this may be a collection of several of Jesus' talks. It is not certain that the entire "sermon" was preached on one day).
18. A learner and helper of Jesus
19. 12
20. About 3 years
21. About 33 years old
22. Joseph of Arimathea
23. Jesus rode into Jerusalem to attend the Passover and the people hailed him with joy and threw branches from the palm trees before him in the street.
24. John the Baptist. At the River Jordan.
25. The disciples began the Christian Church. About six weeks after the death of Jesus.
26. Paul
27. The story of Noah and the flood
28. "In the beginning, God created the heaven and the earth"
29. Daniel
30. Shadrach, Meshach and Abednego
31. Esther
32. Haman
33. Job
34. King David
35. In remembrance of the night when the angel of death passed over the houses of the Hebrews in Egypt and killed the sons of the Egyptians. This was the night Moses led them out from the captivity of Egypt and across the Red Sea a little later.

36. A Jewish church
37. The wise men of the East
38. The boy who gave his lunch of bread and fish to Jesus, from which Jesus miraculously fed 5000 people
39. "Good news." The Gospels tell the story of Jesus,
40. Matthew, Mark, Luke and John
41. Exodus
42. Jacob
43. Palestine—Holy Land—Promised Land—Canaan
44. Ararat, the ark landed. Sinai, Moses received the Ten Commandments. Nebo, Moses died.
45. To be nailed upon a cross, with arms outstretched and left there to die
46. "Father, forgive them for they know not what they do"
47. The last time Jesus and his disciples ever ate together. They were celebrating the Jewish Passover and Jesus had a long farewell talk with them before his death.
48. Ruth
49. David
50. Elisha

## 14. CAN YOU GIVE THE THIRD WORD?

1. Jacob
2. Japheth
3. myrrh
4. hypocrites (Jesus often said it)
5. Abednego
6. Holy Ghost (or Holy Spirit)
7. Leviticus
8. garlic (Foods for which the Hebrews longed in the wilderness. See Numbers 11:5)
9. Judea. (Three main provinces of Palestine in the time of Jesus)
10. Solomon. (Three kings of the United Kingdom)
11. John. (The three disciples most often with Jesus when various Scriptural incidents took place)
12. Fire. (In the story of Elijah on Horeb. The Lord was not in any of them, but the still, small voice came next)

## 15. A QUIZ FOR ADVANCED BIBLE STUDENTS

1. No
2. The books or the library

3. The Old Testament in Hebrew and the New Testament in Greek
4. About 1600 years
5. Probably at least forty different men—poets and prophets, kings and fishermen
6. They were passed from one generation to the next by word of mouth. Tribes who cannot read and write often repeat long stories orally with very little variation, and it is reasonable to suppose that the early Hebrews preserved many phrases and details which later became part of their written record.
7. Copied by hand very slowly and carefully. This made them expensive.
8. They had copies of the Scriptures in their monasteries and they made beautifully wrought books from them, sometimes illuminating the headings in red and blue and gold. A few such copies still exist in museums.
9. Approximately one thousand
10. A missionary must first learn the language of the tribe and if there is no written language he must make one; then he translates the Bible or parts of it; and last he teaches the people to read.
11. Yes. There were several books between Malachi and Matthew, which covered the history of the period between the Old Testament and the New. These may be found in old Bibles.
12. 1189
13. Psalms
14. II John
15. The first five books of the Old Testament. This is the Jewish Torah or Law, considered by the Jews as of supreme worth.
16. The Old Testament was written before Jesus was born and the New Testament was written after Jesus was born.
17. Probably Paul's letters, dating from about 50 A.D. Some scholars believe I Thessalonians is the oldest book in the New Testament.
18. Thirteen. Hebrews, which was once believed to have been one of Paul's letters, is now widely credited to another author.
19. To encourage and to rebuke the new little churches and to settle practical problems for them by his advice.
20. Paul gradually built up a group of trained helpers—such as Timothy, Silas, Priscilla, Aquilla, and others—and when the time came for Paul to move on, he usually left one or more of his assistants in charge of the church he had formed. They reported to him when they could and he kept in touch with the progress and the problems of that church. This is clearly shown in his letters.
21. The Ten Commandments
22. No
23. 36

24. Feeding the 5000
25. Rome built good roads to her remote provinces to maintain commerce and to move her troops when necessary. She discouraged robbers and hold-up bands. Over these roads, with considerable ease and in comparative safety, Paul and the others carried the gospel to the Gentile world. There was a saying, "All roads lead to Rome" and once the Christians established themselves in Rome, the missionary movement made more progress. In addition to good roads, Rome had passenger ships on regular schedules in the Mediterranean and had swept most of the pirates off the seas. 150 years after the crucifixion, Christianity had penetrated to the limits of the mighty Roman Empire.
26. Apparently it helped. It roused the Christians to fight for the cause, even to the death. When they were driven out of one locality they appeared in another and wherever they went they formed new little churches. Persecution spread the story of the Nazarene instead of suppressing it.
27. Matthew. It was written to prove to the Jews that Jesus the crucified was their long-expected Messiah. The key phrase is "that it might be fulfilled," referring to ancient Jewish prophecy
28. Mark. It is the shortest gospel. It spends no time on genealogy but tells the story of the adult Jesus in simple and straight-forward style. Key word is "straightway" which suggests action and progress.
29. Yes. John Mark was a young man of Jerusalem and probably was one of the many disciples of Jesus, beside the famous Twelve. The Last Supper was held in his own home and he followed to Gethsemane and witnessed the arrest of Jesus. (See Mark 14:51-52).
30. Luke
31. Luke. He presents Jesus as the Great Physician
32. Luke was a doctor himself
33. John's Gospel
34. Latin
35. Nero
36. Constantine
37. Underground passages in the city of Rome, used as burial places for the dead and as meeting places for the early Christians during the period of their persecution.
38. According to an ancient tradition, Joseph carried the Holy Grail to England where he built a shrine which later became Glastonbury Cathedral. The Grail became part of the legends of King Arthur.
39. Alfred the Great
40. Martin Luther

41. John Wycliffe made (or started, possibly it was completed by others) the first complete translation of the Bible from the Latin into English. About 1380. Cost approximately $200 per copy.
42. Gutenberg invented modern printing in Germany, 1450. The first complete book printed is said to have been the Bible. Printing was a tremendous advance over copying books by hand, and printing made it possible to produce Bibles in quantities at a greatly reduced cost. Thus the common people could afford the Bible.
43. The version commonly used by the Roman Catholic Church
44. The King James version
45. 1611
46. Moffatt's
47. No. There is no record of Jesus writing, except in the sand
48. A person who travels about distributing or selling religious books and tracts. (colporteur)
49. The Gideons
50. Pure religion and undefiled before God and the Father is this: To visit the fatherless and widows in their affliction, and to keep oneself unspotted from the world. James 1:27

## 16.   CAN YOU IDENTIFY THESE MEN AND WOMEN?

1. Founder of Methodist Church
2. German leader of Protestant Reformation
3. Leader of Salvation Army
4. Social settlement worker; Hull House, Chicago
5. Bohemian reformer and martyr—1415
6. Methodist leader and preacher in John Wesley's time
7. Founder of Christian Endeavor Society
8. Leader of Mormon Church (Latter Day Saints)
9. Franciscan priest associated with the missions of Southern California
10. Founder of Tuskegee Schools
11. Women's Christian Temperance Union
12. Y.M.C.A. leader and evangelist; founder of Northfield School in Massachusetts and Moody Bible Institute of Chicago
13. Orator and anti-Christian lecturer
14. Founder of Christian Science
15. Nurse; American Red Cross
16. Famous preacher at Plymouth Congregational Church, Brooklyn, N.Y.
17. Chinese ethical teacher and philosopher

18. Leader of "bloodless revolution" of the common people of India
19. Swiss Protestant reformer
20. English nurse, "The Lady with the Lamp," Crimean War
21. Founder of Society of Friends (Quakers)
22. English scientist; author of "Origin of Species." His theories of evolution are frowned upon by Christians as being contrary to Genesis
23. Abolitionist and anti-slavery lecturer of Boston
24. Founder of Buddhist religion—about 500 B.C.
25. Founder of Church of the New Jerusalem (Swedish)
26. Author of "The Pilgrim's Progress"
27. British explorer who went to Africa to find Livingstone
28. Brother of John Wesley, associated with early Methodist work, and author of many hymns
29. First Methodist bishop in America
30. Famous Baptist preacher of London, about 1860. He drew tremendous crowds and his books had a wide sale
31. Author of "The Battle Hymn of the Republic"
32. Editor of "Outlook" magazine; succeeded Beecher at Plymouth Church, Brooklyn
33. Greek philosopher and teacher—about 400 B.C.
34. First Roman emperor to encourage Christianity
35. Persecutor of the Christians in Rome
36. Wife of Adoniram Judson, missionary to Burma
37. Founder of "moonlight schools" for the underprivileged white adults of the Kentucky mountains
38. Famous radio preacher
39. English evangelist who toured the United States in recent years
40. Dutch philosopher (Jewish)—1656

## 17. A QUIZ ON RELIGIOUS ART

1. No
2. Mother
3. Raphael
4. Murillo
5. William Holman Hunt
6. Rev. 3:20
7. "Christ and the Doctors" by Hofmann
8. Leonardo da Vinci
9. John the Baptist
10. No beginning, no end
11. John Singer Sargent. Boston Public Library

12. Sir Joshua Reynolds
13. Riverside Church, New York City
14. "The Descent from the Cross"
15. Tissot
16. Michelangelo
17. Titian
18. Raphael
19. Ernst Zimmerman
20. Michelangelo's *The Last Judgment*, Sistine Chapel, Rome


## 18. HIDDEN BOOKS OF THE BIBLE

1. Acts
2. Genesis
3. Luke
4. Esther
5. Hosea
6. Joel
7. Micah
8. Ruth
9. Peter
10. Amos
11. Romans
12. Hebrews
13. Mark
14. Psalms
15. Job


## 19. A QUIZ ON RELIGIOUS LITERATURE

1. Dr. Charles M. Sheldon
2. The three Wise Men
3. Alfred Tennyson. The bar means death.
4. Quo Vadis
5. "Whither Goest Thou?" According to the story, Peter had be-come discouraged with his work and was leaving Rome. On the road he meets a vision of Jesus, and he returns.
6. "Ben-Hur" by General Lew Wallace
7. "I am the captain of my soul." From *Invictus* by William Henley
8. John Greenleaf Whittier
9. *Pilgrim's Progress*
10. William Wordsworth
11. Grey's "Elegy in a Country Churchyard"
12. Bruce Barton. Jesus is the man
13. E. Stanley Jones
14. From "Trees" by Joyce Kilmer
15. Adoniram Judson
16. William Cullen Bryant ."Thanatopsis"

17. The Elsie Dinsmore books
18. Dr. Henry Van Dyke
19. "God bless us every one"
20. The book is by Henry Drummond. The greatest thing is *love,* based upon I Corinthians 13.
21. *Uncle Tom's Cabin* by Harriet Beecher Stowe
22. *The Green Pastures*
23. By unselfish service to others and sharing his own small store
24. "Why the Chimes Rang"
25. Be present at our table, Lord,
    Be here and everywhere adored;
    These creatures bless and grant that we
    May feast in paradise with Thee.


## 20.  A MISSIONARY QUIZ

1. "Go ye into all the world and make disciples of all nations"
2. St. Paul
3. Mark, Silas, Barnabas, Timothy, Luke
4. Peter Parker
5. David Livingstone
6. William Carey
7. John Eliot
8. Spain
9. Because it was largely unexplored and because the natives lived in the darkness of ignorance
10. David Livingstone
11. Adoniram Judson
12. Gen. Samuel Chapman Armstrong
13. Sir Wilfred Grenfell
14. Schools held in the Southern Mountains (Kentucky and adjacent states) to teach adults to read and write. Held on moonlight nights when the people could travel more easily on dark roads and creek beds. Established by Cora Wilson Stewart.
15. a) Judson   b) Livingstone   c) Paton   d) Grenfell
16. Dr. Albert Leroy Shelton
17. Africa
18. Dr. Arthur Jackson
19. John G. Paton
20. Mary Slessor
21. Dr. Theodore Leighton Pennell
22. James Evans
23. Missionary to Uganda, Africa

24. William Carey
25. Bishop Henry Benjamin Whipple
26. Alexander Duff
27. Ion Keith-Falconer
28. Sheldon Jackson


## 21. A QUIZ ON RELIGIOUS MUSIC

1. Fanny Crosby
2. Charles Wesley, brother of John Wesley
3. Martin Luther
4. Homer Rodeheaver
5. Phillips Brooks—"Oh, Little Town of Bethlehem"
6. Singers who go about the streets at Christmas singing carols
7. "The Old Rugged Cross"
8. "Nearer, My God, to Thee"
9. They sang them. Psalms is called the Hymn Book of the Bible
10. They learned them by heart, by chanting them after the cantor. Many of the psalms are so arranged that the chief singer sings the important words and the congregation repeats at intervals a sort of chorus of the same phrase, such as "Praise ye the Lord"
11. The chief singer in a Jewish church
12. The Scots
13. Cardinal John Henry Newman of the Roman Church
14. "Silent Night, Holy Night"
15. The Diamond Jubilee of Queen Victoria
16. Sir Arthur Sullivan, of Gilbert and Sullivan fame
17. Julia Ward Howe
18. "Jerusalem the Golden"
19. "Jesus, Savior, Pilot Me"
20. "From Heaven Above to Earth I Come"
21. "Praise God from whom all blessings flow"
22. "Faith of our Fathers"
23. An oratorio
24. Yes. They sang a hymn before they went out after the Last Supper. Matt. 26:30 and Mark 14:26
25. Ira D. Sankey


## 22. QUESTIONS FOR WELL-INFORMED CHRISTIANS

1. A preacher who traveled over a large territory ... usually by horseback ... and preached at many settlements in rotation. It

might have taken him weeks or months to complete the circuit, then he started around again

2. No. A sky pilot is a slang term for a minister
3. George Whitefield
4. Riverside Church
5. Roger Williams
6. Rev. Cotton Mather
7. Universal
8. It is the eve of All Saints Day (Nov. 1)
9. Just before Ash Wednesday, the beginning of Lent. Mardi Gras is a festival of foolishness and gaiety, which is followed by the solemn Lenten season
10. No
11. Statement of belief. The word is from the Latin *credo*, "I believe"
12. No. The Apostles' Creed dates back to about the 5th century
13. The basement section, especially under the altar. In some churches this was a burial place. In modern churches it is often a vestry or chapel
14. A famous church architect, noted for the grace and symmetry of his slender steeples
15. The redbud tree, common in Virginia and thereabouts. The legend is that this is the tree from which Judas hanged himself. The tree was so ashamed of him that its white blossoms blushed pink and have remained that way ever since
16. To find David Livingstone
17. Billy Sunday
18. Utah
19. By the Jewish star of David (6 pointed)
20. Haile Selassie
21. A person who regularly gives one tenth of his income to the church or to charities
22. A movement started at Morgan Memorial in Boston, where bags of discarded clothing, old furniture, newspapers, anything at all—are brought to the institution, salvaged by paid workers, and the products resold through retail stores at very low prices to poor people. This idea has spread to many other cities and the units are known as The Goodwill Industries. Their slogan is, "Not charity but a chance" and they provide work for thousands of poor but self-respecting people; they also maintain day nurseries, summer camps, and a varied program of social service.
23. Yes. It is said that the entire prayer has been written on the back of a postage stamp, scratched on the head of a pin and otherwise put into very small space. One of the monotype companies has put the prayer in type form on a single piece of

metal the size of one type letter. All of these must be read under the microscope.

24. Cologne Cathedral
25. A gigantic statue on the border between Chile and Argentine in the Andes—a symbol of peace between the two countries, paid for by the women of both countries and made from bronze obtained by melting down old cannon. It was placed on the boundary which had been disputed by both countries.
26. The first Roman Bible, translated by St. Jerome into Latin
27. Geneva Bible, 1560. In the story of Adam and Eve it reads, "They made themselves breeches out of leaves"
28. Matthew, Mark and Luke. These are similar in style and record, with many passages nearly identical. John is different.
29. A tale of woe—from the lamentations of Jeremiah
30. The Old North Church

## 23.    THESE ARE "STICKERS"

1. A young Greek who came to rule Palestine about 168 B.C. and spent six years trying to force the Greek religion upon his Jewish subjects at the point of a bayonet. He polluted the Temple at Jerusalem by sacrificing swine upon the altar and committed other outrages.
2. A patriotic family who led a noble attempt to win Jewish independence. Hailed as national heroes, their story is told in the book of Maccabees found in old Bibles between the Old Testament and the New.
3. King of Assyria who invaded Palestine about 730 B.C.
4. II Kings 20:7
5. Rom. 16
6. II John
7. A Christian scribe or secretary who did the actual writing of some of Paul's letters.
8. The captives returned from Babylon
9. Peter
10. A measure equal to about 11 bushels
11. Ephesus, Smyrna, Pergamos, Thyatira, Sardis, Philadelphia, Laodicea (Rev. 1:11)
12. After 1611, the date of the King James version, older manuscripts closer to the original Hebrew and Greek came to light, so that more accurate translations can now be made.
13. The Sinaitic manuscript discovered at St. Catherine's Convent, Mount Sinai, 1844. Parts are missing, of course,

14. A friend of Luke to whom he dedicated his two books—the Gospel of Luke and Acts
15. Asenath
16. Fire and Famine, Disease and Death (Conquest is sometimes given instead of fire)
17. Sisera
18. Paul and Silas
19. Symbolic battleground between Good and Evil (Rev. 16:16). Based on the battle of Megiddo in which Sisera was defeated.
20. Genesis and John's Gospel

## 24.  DO YOU KNOW YOUR HYMNS?

1. All our sins and griefs to bear
2. With the cross of Jesus going on before
3. But that thy blood was shed for me
4. From India's coral strand
5. The day of march has come
6. Of Jesus and His glory, of Jesus and His love
7. Joyful and triumphant
8. Bearing gifts, we travel afar
9. There's a mother's deep prayer, and a baby's low cry
10. Much we need thy tender care
11. Stood an old rugged cross
12. E'en though it be a cross that raiseth me
13. Over life's tempestuous sea
14. Waving Christ's own soldiers to their home on high
15. That glorious song of old
16. For yielding is sin
17. When at evening the sun goeth down?
18. When I am safe on that beautiful shore
19. That calls us from a world of care
20. No tender voice like thine can peace afford
21. What its signs of promise are
22. Care for the dying
23. When on others thou art calling, do not pass me by
24. May we like Magdalene lay at thy feet
25. Where sound the cries of race and clan
26. Early in the morning our song shall rise to thee
27. Our hope for years to come
28. Like the wideness of the sea
29. Glory to the Lord on high
30. But it is fed and watered by God's almighty hand
31. All nature sings, and round me rings the music of the spheres

32. Above the stable while the angels sing
33. Forgive our feverish ways
34. Come unto me and rest
35. Shadows of the evening steal across the sky
36. Heaven is touching earth with rest
37. With one accord, our parting hymn of praise
38. As thou didst break the loaves beside the sea
39. Day by day His sweet voice soundeth
      Saying, "Christian, follow me"
40. We will be true to thee till death (refrain)
41. His blood-red banner streams afar,
      Who follows in His train?
42. Ye soldiers of the cross
43. In lowly paths of service free
44. Let it float
45. To tell to all the world that God is light
46. For purple mountain majesties
      Above the fruited plain
47. He is trampling out the vintage where the grapes of wrath are stored
48. O'er earth's green fields and ocean's wave-beat shore
49. Is Jesus Christ her Lord
50. Our hearts in Christian love
51. Does his successive journeys run
52. The church our blest Redeemer saved with his own precious blood
53. Pilgrim through this barren land
54. Lead thou me on
55. To serve thee to the end
56. Glory to the newborn King
57. Let me hide myself in thee
58. On which the prince of glory died
59. Towering o'er the wrecks of time
60. As it was in the beginning, is now and ever shall be,
      World without end. Amen

## 26. A SIMPLE BIBLE ALPHABET FOR JUNIORS

| | | | | |
|---|---|---|---|---|
| Adam | Grapes | Miriam | Samson | Zion |
| Baal | Hannah | Noah | Ten | |
| Cain | Isaac | Orpah | Unclean | |
| David | Joshua | Peter | Vashti | |
| Egypt | King | Quail | Washed | |
| Faith | Luke | Rachel | Years | |

## 27. WHICH WORD IS OUT OF PLACE?

1. ark
2. gallows
3. snow
4. shepherds
5. leprosy
6. Ezekiel
7. Micah
8. Lazarus
9. Joppa
10. Lot
11. Ahab
12. Acts
13. Joel
14. Nineveh
15. saxaphone
16. Ur
17. tiger
18. Everest
19. pistol
20. chariot
21. ephod (priest's robe)
22. Jesse
23. Jezebel
24. tabernacle
25. temple

## 28. MY STORY OF JOSEPH

Twelve — Joseph — coat — colors — jealous — pit — sold — Egypt — coat — blood — a beast had killed him.

Servant — captain — woman — prison — good — keeper — prisoners — butler — baker — dreams — did.

Cows — ears of corn — Joseph — prison — years — good crops — seven — famine — barns — grain — starve — clothes — finger — chariot.

Brothers — Egypt — corn — them — know him — Benjamin — Benjamin — take care of him.

Brothers — food — servant — cup — Benjamin's — cup — slave — cup — sack — Benjamin — Joseph — Egypt.

## 29. TEN BIBLE TRIANGLES

1. **J**
   **O**G
   **SE**A
   **E**VIL
   **P**ETER
   **H**EAVEN

2. **C**
   **A**S
   **R**ED
   **P**ALM
   **E**MPTY
   **N**AAMAN
   **T**IMOTHY
   **E**PISTLES
   **R**EVERENCE

3.  **M**
    **A**S
    **NOT**
    **NEBO**
    **A**ARON

4.  **V**
    **IS**
    **NET**
    **E**YES
    **GR**AVE
    **A**NOINT
    **R**AIMENT

5.  **T**
    **A**M
    **B**ED
    **E**SAU
    **R**ISEN
    **NEEDLE**
    **A**POSTLE
    **CHARIOTS**
    **L**AMENTING
    **E**NCOURAGED

6.  **A**
    **HE**
    **A**NT
    **S**ANG
    **U**NCLE
    **E**STHER
    **RE**JOICE
    **U**NLAWFUL
    **S**WADDLING

7.  **B**
    **E**R
    **A**SK
    **T**OIL
    **I**DOLS
    **T**ICKET
    **U**NKNOWN
    **D**ISCIPLE
    **E**GYPTIANS
    **S**YNAGOGUES

8.  **T**
    **R**E
    **E**WE
    **S**HOE
    **PE**ACE
    **A**THENS
    **S**OLOMON
    **S**OLDIERS
    **E**THOPIAN
    **S**TRENGTHEN

9.  **Z**
    **A**I
    **C**UT
    **C**OAT
    **H**EROD
    **E**LISHA
    **U**NCLEAN
    **S**TRENGTH

10. **M**
    **U**S
    **L**AD
    **T**OWN
    **I**SAAC
    **T**HRONE
    **U**PRIGHT
    **D**ISEASES
    **E**LEPHANTS

## 30.  WHO? WHAT? WHERE? WHICH?

1.  Jacob—angels—ladder—to heaven
2.  Seven priests—trumpets—seven times—Jericho
3.  The priest and the Levite—the man who had fallen among thieves—on the other side
4.  The Good Samaritan—bound up his wounds—to the Inn—"Take care of him and I will pay you"
5.  Elisha—Elijah—heaven—chariot of fire
6.  John the Baptist—at the Jordan River—lachet—shoe
7.  Samson—lion—swarm—bees
8.  Nehemiah—captivity in Babylon—Jerusalem
9.  Darius—Daniel—lions
10.  Israelites—God—manna
11.  Absalom—revolt—tree—hair
12.  Ruth—Moab—Boaz—gleaner
13.  Jonah—three—fish
14.  Jacob—Esau—blessing
15.  Belshazzar—hand—words—wall
16.  Jordan—John the Baptist—Jesus
17.  Elijah—prophets of Baal—Carmel
18.  Moses—Israelites—forty—Promised Land
19.  Moses—Nebo
20.  Israelites—Red—Pharaoh's
21.  Haman—gallows
22.  Jesus—five loaves—two fishes
23.  David—Uriah—marry Uriah's wife
24.  Esther—Ahasuerus—Jews—golden sceptre
25.  Pharaoh—fat cows—thin cows—Joseph